Melissa's Magnificent Message

Author **Frank Glew**

Illustrator **Sheila King**

The breezes,
the tree,
the honey bee.
All volunteers.
— Juliet Russell Lowel

Human beings have fabricated the illusion that in the 21st century
they have the technology prowess to be independent of nature.
Bees underline the reality that we are more, not less, dependent
on nature's service in a world of close to 7 billion people. — Achim Steiner UNEP

Bumble Island was the happy land of bees and honey. Thousands of wild animals and beautiful plants lived there. Majestic Melissa was one of the animals. She had five strange eyes and six very hairy legs. Melissa was a Honey Bee, a very wise **Honey Bee!** Sadly, no one knew that without Melissa, Bumble Island would be a huge disaster.

All of the Bumble Island animals had plenty of good food and clean water. The scent of wild flowers floated through the air. Melissa buzzed happily around the flowers singing a funny rap: **"You can always eat our honey but you can never eat your money."**

You can always eat our honey but you can never eat your money!

Everyone wondered why she sang this weird song.

3

Using her four fast wings, Melissa darted around
Bumble Island visiting her best friend, the Monarch
Butterfly. Melissa became famous in all parts
of the island for her wacky dance and odd song.
Many animals called her Meli, which means honey.

4

On her rear end, Meli hid a long, barbed, poisonous stinger that could spring out like a cat's claw. Some people screamed and dashed away the moment they saw her. Meli was surprised because she would not sting anyone unless she was protecting her family.

Each day Meli performed her magic while visiting flowers. She gathered golden pollen from the flowers and stuffed it in her leg baskets. She shared the pollen with other flowers. This was called pollination.

As she worked, Meli sang her funky rap: **"You can always eat our honey but you can never eat your money."**

No one understood this freaky song.

As Meli worked, she became happier and happier.
Pollination was her most important job.
Plants treated her with sweet nectar
so she could make honey.

Again Meli sang her silly rap:
**"You can always eat our honey but you
can never eat your money."**

The animals were curious
why she sang this kooky song.

7

Trees such as apple, peach and cherry were visited. All flowers needed to be pollinated or they would not grow into fruit. Meli and her sisters raced to visit each flower on every tree.

8

You can always eat our honey

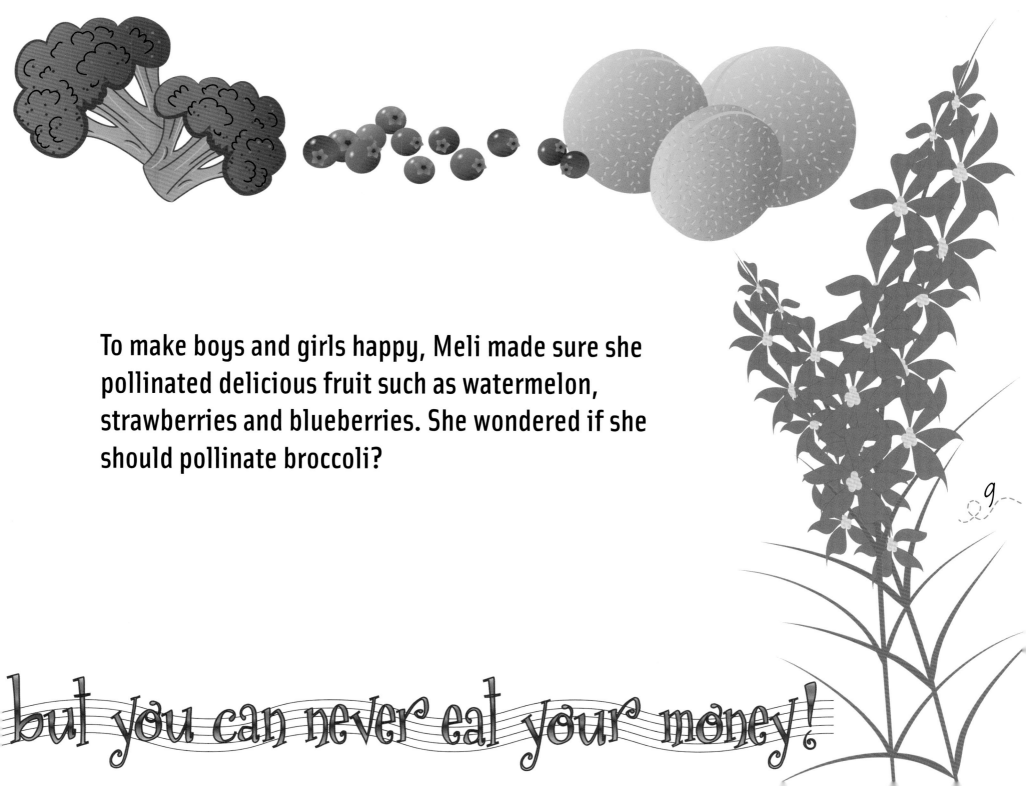

To make boys and girls happy, Meli made sure she pollinated delicious fruit such as watermelon, strawberries and blueberries. She wondered if she should pollinate broccoli?

but you can never eat your money!

Bumble Island was such a bee-utiful and amazing place to live that everyone wanted to live there. Many new babies were born. More people meant more food was needed.

10

To make more food and more money, insects that ate farmers' crops needed to be stopped. New chemicals were made to get rid of the pesky insects. City people used the chemicals on their lawns and gardens. Insects eating any part of the plants, including the pollen, were poisoned.

11

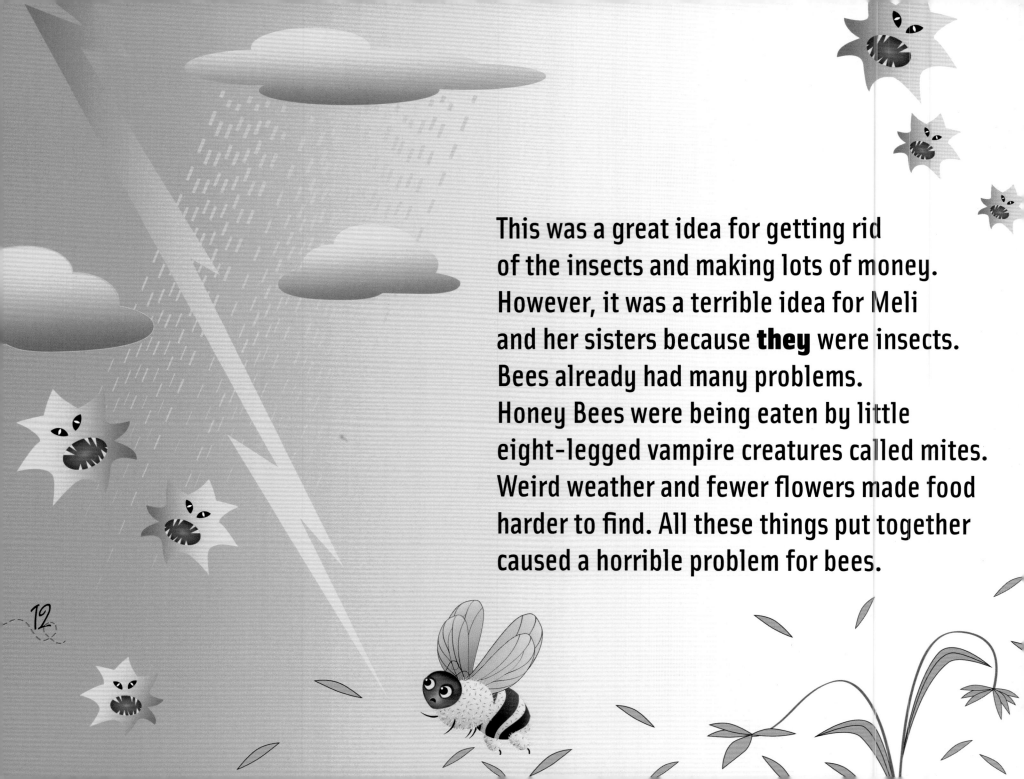

This was a great idea for getting rid of the insects and making lots of money. However, it was a terrible idea for Meli and her sisters because **they** were insects. Bees already had many problems. Honey Bees were being eaten by little eight-legged vampire creatures called mites. Weird weather and fewer flowers made food harder to find. All these things put together caused a horrible problem for bees.

In a short time there were fewer and fewer insects. Honey Bees, bumble bees, butterflies, ladybugs and dragonflies were all insects!

Meli was bee-wildered. She knew that without bees there would be much less food and people might starve.

13

F. Frog

Rob Wren

Father Longlegs

B.B. Bee

M. Moth

GROCERIES

CLOSED

As the bees disappeared so did many plants and animals including birds and frogs. Sadly, the grocery stores started running out of good food! Parents were worried about feeding their children. Bumble Island was in **big** trouble.

FOR SALE

Meli warned the Bumble Island leaders about this serious food problem. She asked them to make new ways to grow food that did not harm all animals.

She sang her peculiar rap even louder: **"You can always eat our honey but you can never eat your money."**

Still no one understood Melissa's magnificent message.

MOVED

To brighten up dull lawns in the cities, Meli wished people would grow flower gardens and vegetable gardens without using poisons. Insects like her friend the Monarch Butterfly would easily find food. Honey Bees would pollinate the plants and make honey. This would help everyone.

At first no one listened to Meli. The Bumble Island leaders needed good advice. Scientists were asked to study this serious problem. The leaders were bee-dazzled when scientists totally agreed with Meli. Too much good food would be lost without bees and other insects.

17

After many meetings, the wise leaders soon decided that Meli was right. Healthy food and nature were much more important than a few people making tons of money.

All of a sudden her lesson: **"You can always eat our honey but you can never eat your money,"** began to make sense.

The Bumble Island leaders now understood that without insects like Meli and her sisters, there would be fewer plants. Fewer plants meant much less food. Bumble Island might become as barren as the moon because everything was connected. This was everyone's problem.

People in the cities enjoyed making bee friendly gardens on their lawns. They grew sunflowers, vegetables, daisies and milkweed. Roadsides looked like colourful rainbow ribbons. Beekeepers started raising bees in the city! The bees were pleased to pollinate the many different flowers.

20

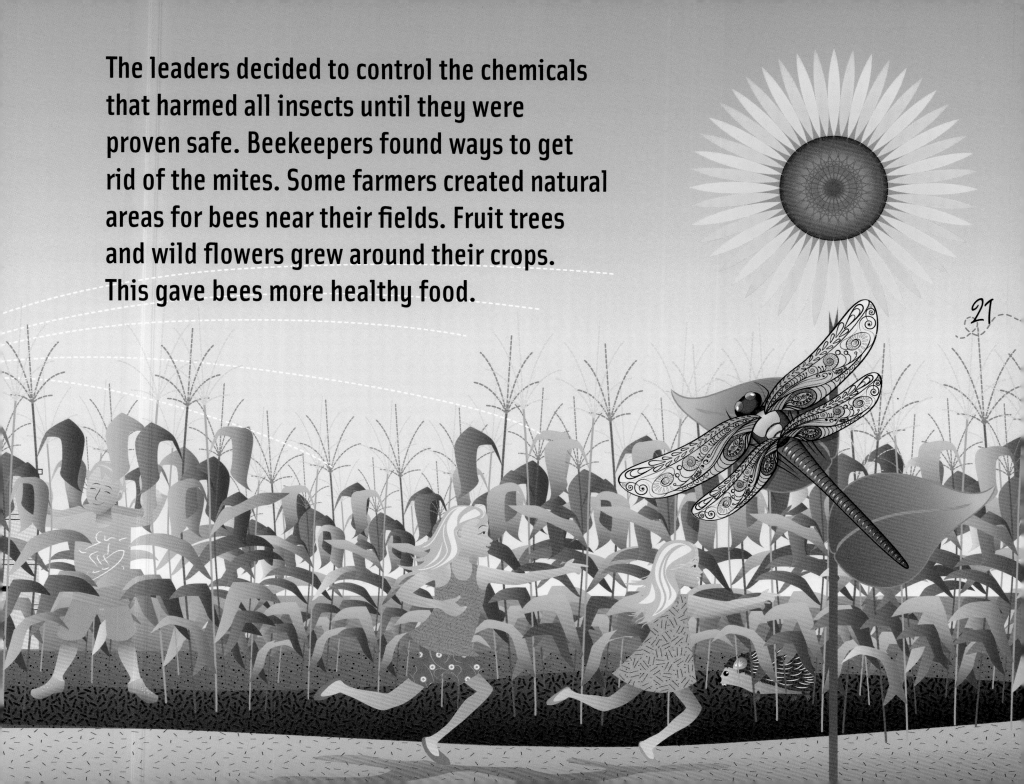

The leaders decided to control the chemicals that harmed all insects until they were proven safe. Beekeepers found ways to get rid of the mites. Some farmers created natural areas for bees near their fields. Fruit trees and wild flowers grew around their crops. This gave bees more healthy food.

21

School children were happy to make natural areas on their playgrounds. Monarch Butterflies were thrilled to find milkweed for laying their eggs. Ladybugs and birds ate insects that nibbled on garden plants. Meli and her sisters enjoyed working overtime visiting all the new flowers. Everyone worked together to make Bumble Island a better home.

Once again, Bumble Island became a wonderful place to live.
Everyone learned a most important lesson from Melissa.
There are many, many things much more important
than making piles of money.

Finally everyone understood her clever message:
**"You can always eat our honey but you can
never, ever, ever eat your money."**

Magnificent Melissa saved Bumble Island.

No bees, no honey; no work, no money. – Ancient Proverb

90% of fruits and vegetables depend on bees for pollination

Pollen leg baskets

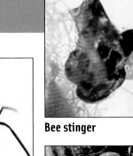
Bee stinger

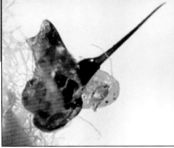

Bee's hairy head and tongue

Mites on bees

Pollen sticks to the bees hairy body

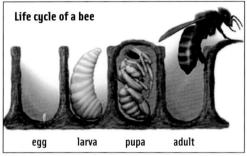
Life cycle of a bee

egg   larva   pupa   adult

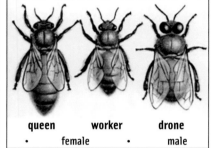

queen   worker   drone
• female   • male

Honey

The average worker bee makes about 1/12th of a teaspoon of honey in her lifetime. Bees gather sweet nectar with their long tongue. After they process the nectar in their stomach, they regurgitate it into the honeycomb cells. Then they fan the cells with their wings to remove excess moisture. The final result is honey.

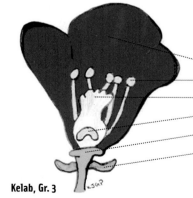

Parts of a flower

- petal
- anther (boy part)
- stigma
- ovary (girl part)
- nectary (forms nectar to attract bees)
- sepal

Kelab, Gr. 3

anther

Honey Bee pollination

Pollen from the anther (male part) of the first plant is carried to the stigma (female part) of the second plant. Pollen goes down to the ovary where it forms a seed, fruit or vegetable.

Kalista, Gr. 3

stigma

Sophie, Gr. 2

Unique among all God's creatures, only the honeybee improves the environment and preys not on any other species.
– Royden Brown